D1482205

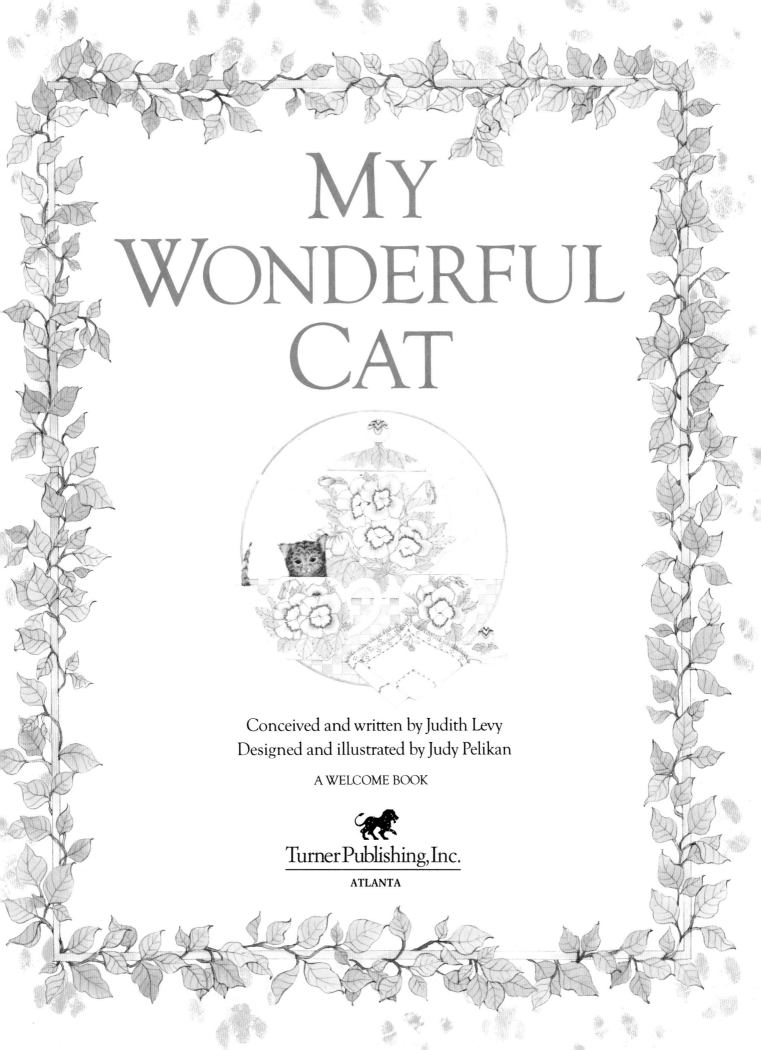

MY WONDERFUL CAT

Conceived and written by Judith Levy
Designed and illustrated by Judy Pelikan

A WELCOME BOOK

Turner Publishing, Inc.
ATLANTA

CATUS NIPUS

FELINE FLIPUS

Text copyright © 1993 by Judith Levy
Illustrations copyright © 1993 by Pelikan Inc.

Published by Turner Publishing, Inc.
A Subsidiary of Turner Broadcasting System, Inc.
One CNN Center, Box 105366
Atlanta, Georgia 30348-5366

Produced by Welcome Enterprises, Inc.
164 East 95th Street
New York, New York 10128

Distributed by Andrews and McMeel
4900 Main Street
Kansas City, Missouri 64112

Library of Congress Catalog Card Number: 92-85579

Printed in Singapore by Toppan Printing Co., Inc.
1 3 5 7 9 10 8 6 4 2

ISBN 1-878685-41-4

Welcome!

With one little purr
Right from the start,
This soft ball of fur
Crept into my heart.

PICTURE OF MY CAT

Date _____

Table of Contents

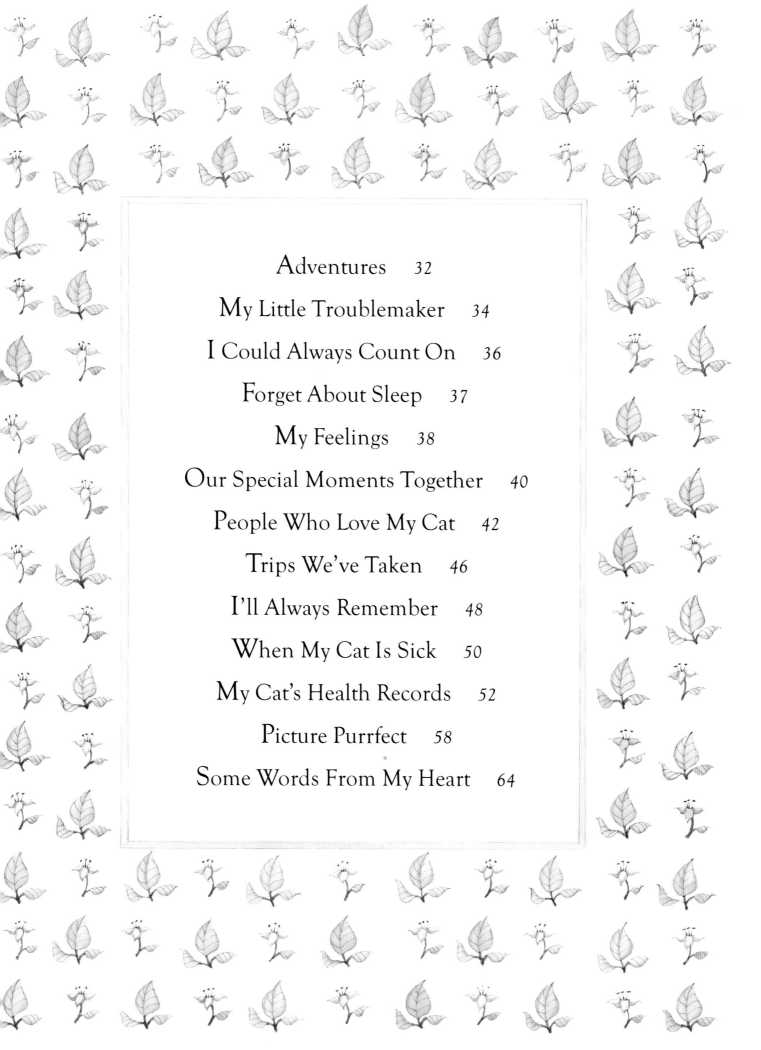

Quotable Cats

"A house without a cat, and a well-fed, well-petted, and properly revered cat, may be a perfect house, perhaps, but how can it prove its title?!"
　　—Mark Twain

"The gingham dog went 'Bow-wow-wow!'
And the calico cat replied 'mee-ow!'
The air was littered, an hour or so,
With bits of gingham and calico..."
　　—Eugene Field, from *The Duel*

"A cat may look on a king."
　　—*Proverbs*

In a cat's eyes, all things belong to cats.
　　—English proverb

"It is a very inconvenient habit of kittens (Alice had once made the remark) that, whatever you say to them they *always* purr."
　　—Lewis Carroll, *Through the Looking Glass*

"Pussy cat, pussy cat,
Where have you been?

I've been to London
To visit the Queen."
    —Mother Goose

"The more you rub a cat on the rump,
The higher she sets her tail."
    —John Ray, *English Proverbs*

"The cat is mighty dignified
Until the dog comes by."
    —Southern folk saying

A favorite cat quote of mine is:

_____

_____

_____

_____

_____

Cats of the World

Oh, decisions aren't easy
For most people, I suppose.
But I sure picked a winner
In the cat that I chose.

Longhair Cats

American Curl

Balinese

Birman

British Turkish Cat

Cymric

Himalayan

Javanese

Kashmir

Maine Coon Cat

Norwegian Forest Cat

Oriental Longhair

Persian

Ragdoll

Somali

Tiffany

Turkish Angora

Turkish Van Cat

Shorthair Cats

Abyssinian	Korat
American Curl Shorthair	Malayan
American Shorthair	Manx
Bombay	Oriental Shorthair
British Shorthair	Rex
Chartreux	Russian Blue
Colorpoint Shorthair	Scottish Fold
Egyptian Mau	Siamese
Exotic Shorthair	Singapura
European Shorthair	Snowshoe
Havana Brown	Sphynx
Japanese Bobtail	Tonkinese

My cat's breed is

_____

Favorite Cat Names

Angel	Ginger	Pepper	Shadow
Boots	Kitty	Princess	Simon
Calico	Lucky	Puff	Smoky
Charlie	Max	Pumpkin	Socrates
Ebony	Mickey	Rex	Tabitha
Felix	Misty	Rusty	Tiger
Fluffy	Muffin	Samantha	Tom

And Some Cat Names of Note

Figaro   Geppetto's cat in *Pinocchio*
Mehitabel   From Don Marquis's *Archy and Mehitabel*
Dinah   Alice's cat in *Through the Looking Glass*
Pyewacket   The cat in *Bell, Book and Candle*
Cosmic Creepers   The cat in *Bedknobs and Broomsticks*
Rhubarb   From *Rhubarb*
Slats & Tanner   MGM's lions

Naming My Cat

I thought of several names,
But they just weren't it.
Then suddenly the right one,
A really purrfect fit.

My cat's name is _____

_____

That name was chosen because _____

_____

_____

_____

Nicknames I call my cat are _____

_____

_____

_____

13

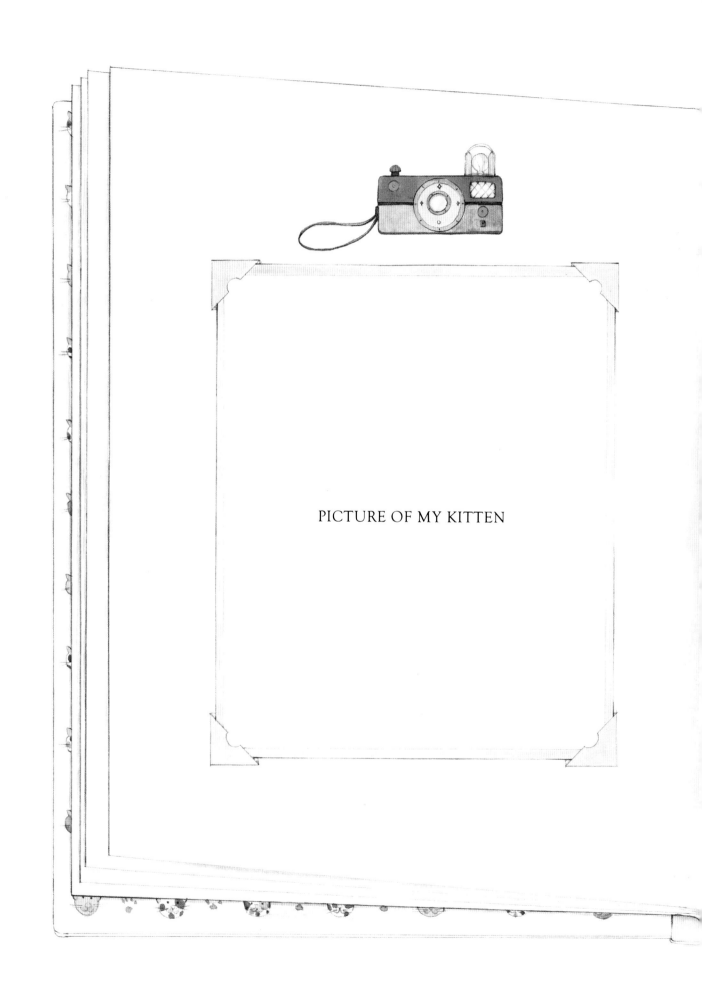

PICTURE OF MY KITTEN

Vital Statistics

Little things like tall and small,
My kitten's weight, and such,
Are special to remember
Because I care so much.

My cat was born

Where _____

When _____

Fur color _____

Eye color _____

My cat's most distinguishing features are _____

_____

_____

_____

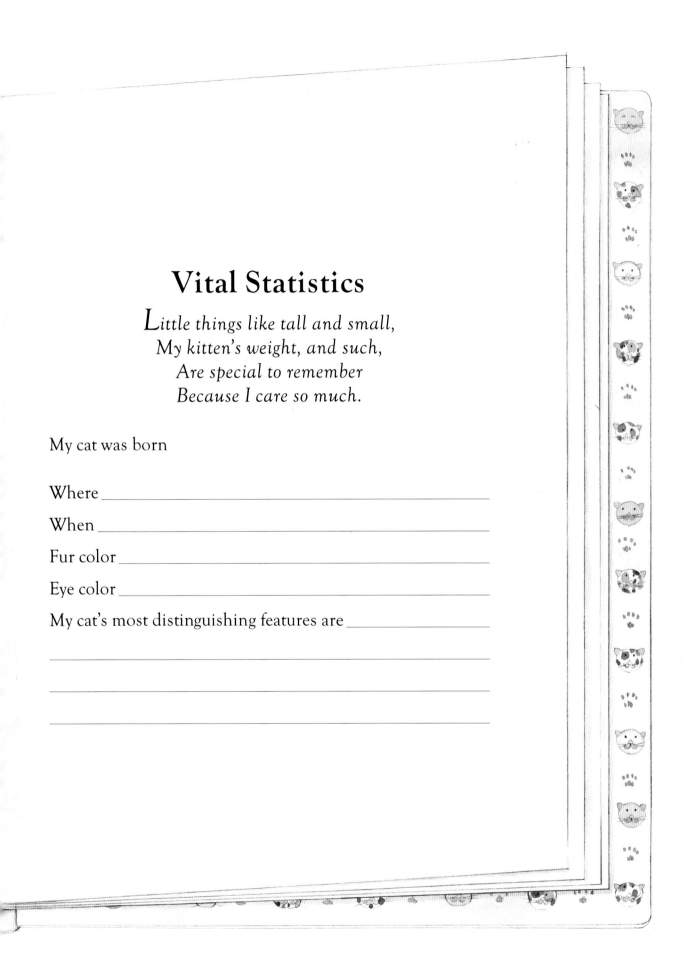

Our First Day

Meowing for attention,
My kitten seemed to say,
"I'm a member of the family,
And I'm here to stay."

My cat moved in at the age of _____

_____

I acquired my cat in this way _____

_____

_____

_____

_____

I'll always remember that first day because _____

_____

_____

_____

_____

The first thing my cat did was _____

_____

_____

_____

_____

I loved my cat right away because _____

_____

_____

_____

_____

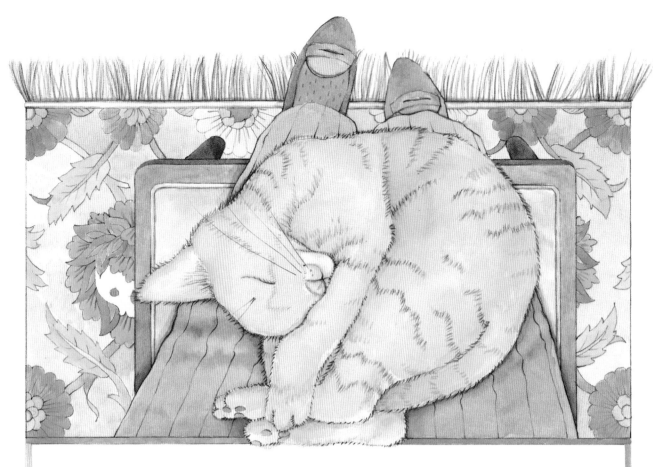

Bonding

Personality plus
And cute as can be.
This sweet little kitten
Now belongs to me.

My first impressions were _____

_____

_____

_____

_____

_____

_____

I knew this cat was special because _____

_____

_____

_____

_____

My cat's personality can best be described as _____

_____

_____

_____

_____

My cat has made my life richer because _____

_____

_____

_____

_____

I knew there was a bond between us when _____

_____

_____

_____

_____

PICTURE OF MY KITTEN

My kitten was most adorable when _____

_____

_____

_____

_____

My kitten was incredibly curious about_____

_____

_____

_____

_____

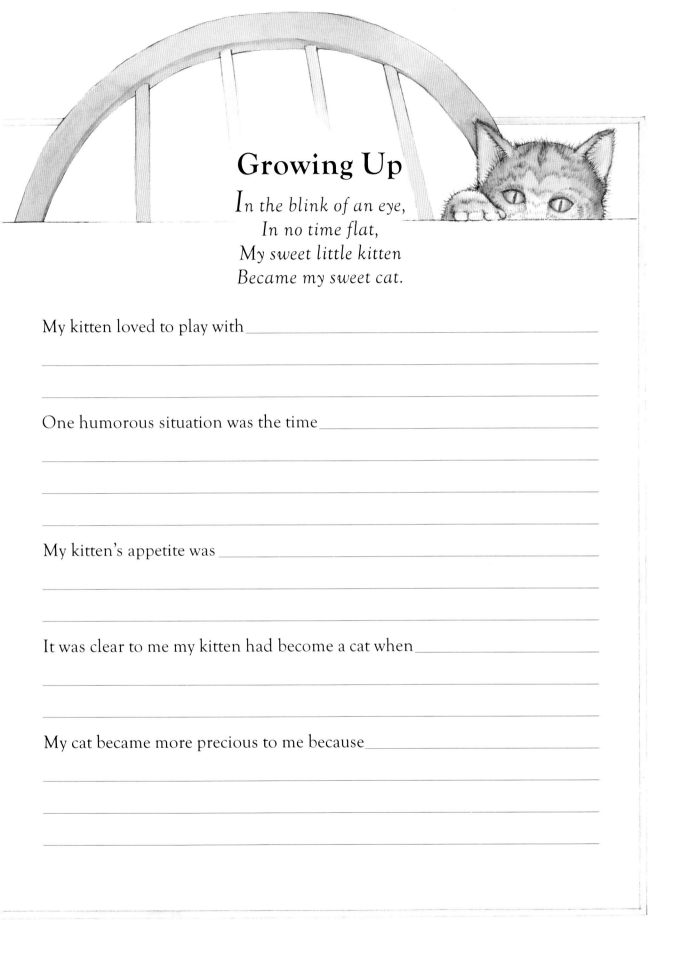

Growing Up

In the blink of an eye,
In no time flat,
My sweet little kitten
Became my sweet cat.

My kitten loved to play with _____

_____

_____

One humorous situation was the time _____

_____

_____

_____

My kitten's appetite was _____

_____

_____

It was clear to me my kitten had become a cat when _____

_____

_____

My cat became more precious to me because _____

_____

_____

_____

PICTURE OF MY
CAT EATING

My cat's favorite meal is _____

_____

_____

_____

I know my cat is hungry when _____

_____

_____

_____

22

So, What's for Dinner?

"Finicky" is not the word.
"Selective" is what I'd say.
A purr means I've pleased
My feline gourmet.

My cat absolutely refuses to eat_____

_____

_____

_____

What a mess my cat made the time_____

_____

_____

_____

_____

A treat my cat loves is_____

_____

_____

_____

23

My Cat's Territory

No matter what I say,
It's the place to "snooze it."
And though it's off-limits,
My cat will always choose it.

My cat's bed is _____

_____

But I can usually find my cat sleeping _____

_____

_____

I have rules about my cat not being on the _____

_____

_____

_____

My cat's favorite hiding place is _____

_____

_____

_____

PICTURE OF MY CAT
CONTENTEDLY SLEEPING

A favorite forbidden spot is _____

_____

_____

But the best spot of all is _____

_____

_____

25

BEAUTIFUL PICTURE
OF MY CAT

Preening

A clean coat's important,
So my cat takes the time.
It's worth all the effort.
Wow! That coat's going to shine.

When it comes to licking, my cat _____

_____

_____

When it comes to being brushed, my cat _____

_____

_____

When it comes to shedding, my cat _____

_____

_____

The worst my cat ever looked was when _____

_____

_____

I know my cat likes to be clean because _____

_____

_____

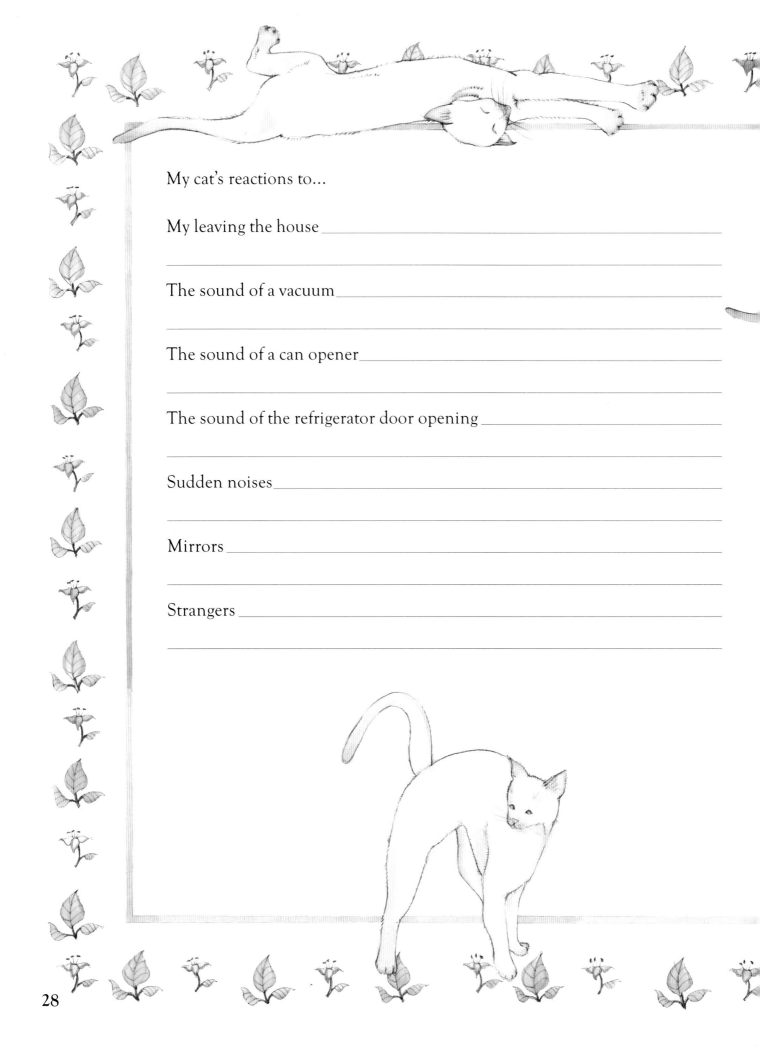

My cat's reactions to...

My leaving the house _____

_____

The sound of a vacuum _____

_____

The sound of a can opener _____

_____

The sound of the refrigerator door opening _____

_____

Sudden noises _____

_____

Mirrors _____

_____

Strangers _____

_____

Reactions

Though cats are unpredictable,
As people often say,
Whenever these things happen,
My cat reacts this way.

Mischievous children _____

_____

Birds _____

_____

Dogs _____

_____

Other cats _____

_____

Behavior

*You can be certain
As night follows day,
My cat is determined
To act just this way.*

When excited, my cat _____

_____

_____

When annoyed, my cat _____

_____

_____

When in a strange house, my cat _____

_____

_____

My cat will bolt whenever _____

_____

_____

When it comes to catnip, my cat _____

_____

_____

When it comes to being scratched, my cat _____

_____

_____

PICTURE OF MY CAT
MAKING MISCHIEF

When contented, my cat _____

_____

_____

My cat is fascinated by _____

_____

_____

Adventures

*I've got to be careful
Or quick as a light,
My cat might dart off
Straight into the night.*

My cat's greatest adventure was _____

_____

_____

_____

_____

_____

_____

When it comes to prowling, my cat _____

_____

_____

_____

My cat once caught _____

_____

_____

_____

Places my cat loves to explore are _____

_____

_____

_____

The longest my cat stayed away was _____

_____

_____

_____

I knew my cat would be back because _____

_____

_____

_____

I think my cat would love to _____

_____

_____

_____

My cat's favorite plaything is _____

_____

_____

My cat likes to nibble on _____

_____

_____

I know when my cat's done something wrong because _____

_____

_____

The biggest crash I ever heard came when my cat _____

_____

_____

I once lost my cool when my cat _____

_____

_____

_____

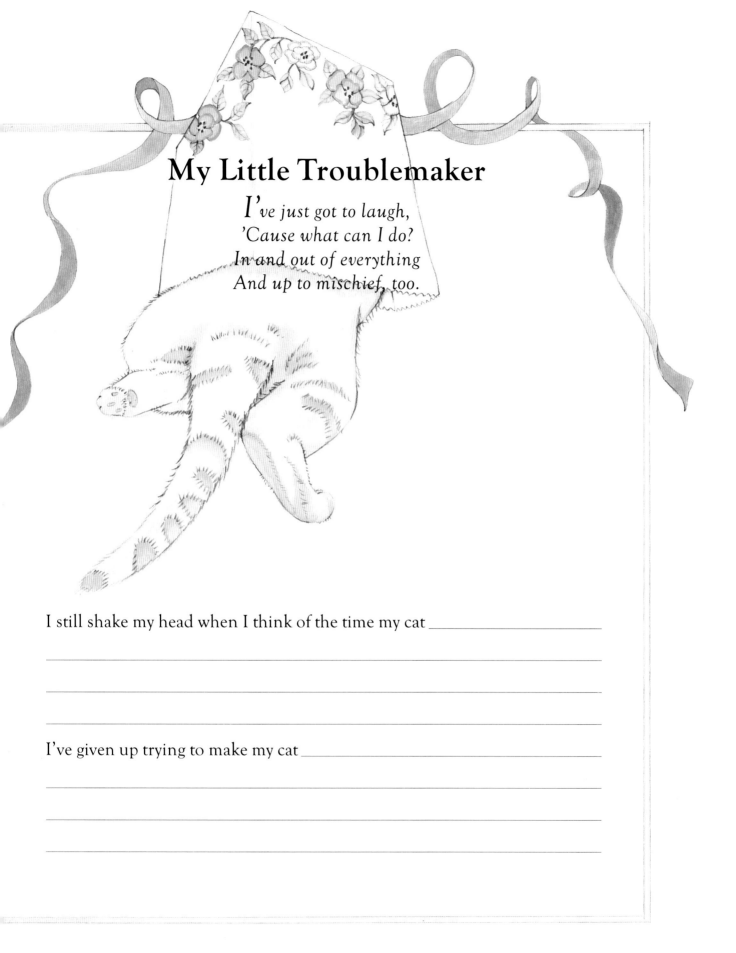

My Little Troublemaker

I've just got to laugh,
'Cause what can I do?
In and out of everything
And up to mischief, too.

I still shake my head when I think of the time my cat _____

_____

_____

_____

I've given up trying to make my cat _____

_____

_____

_____

I Could Always Count On

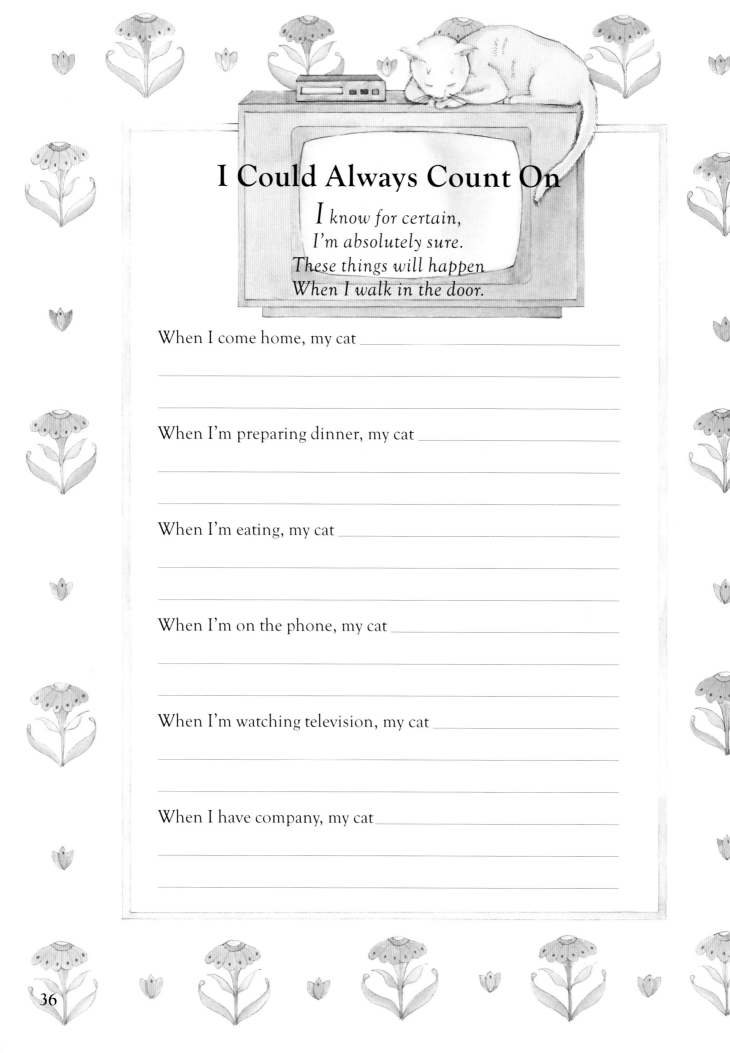

I know for certain,
I'm absolutely sure.
These things will happen
When I walk in the door.

When I come home, my cat _____

_____

When I'm preparing dinner, my cat _____

_____

When I'm eating, my cat _____

_____

When I'm on the phone, my cat _____

_____

When I'm watching television, my cat _____

_____

When I have company, my cat _____

_____

Forget About Sleep

So comfy and cozy,
I could sleep for a year.
But that just won't happen
'Cause my little cat's here.

When I'm in bed, my cat _____

_____

_____

_____

_____

Once, in the middle of the night, my cat _____

_____

_____

_____

My cat likes to wake me up by _____

_____

_____

_____

_____

My Feelings

Sometimes I hide my feelings
So others cannot see.
But my precious cat knows
And always comforts me.

When I'm feeling blue, my cat _____

_____

_____

When I'm in a bad mood, my cat _____

_____

_____

I was really touched when my cat _____

_____

_____

My feelings about my cat can best be expressed this way _____

_____

_____

_____

_____

Sometimes all I have to do is look at my cat and I feel

_____

_____

_____

_____

_____

I always feel good when I can do this for my cat

_____

_____

_____

_____

My cat has enriched my life because_____

_____

_____

_____

_____

The thing I love best about my cat is_____

_____

_____

_____

_____

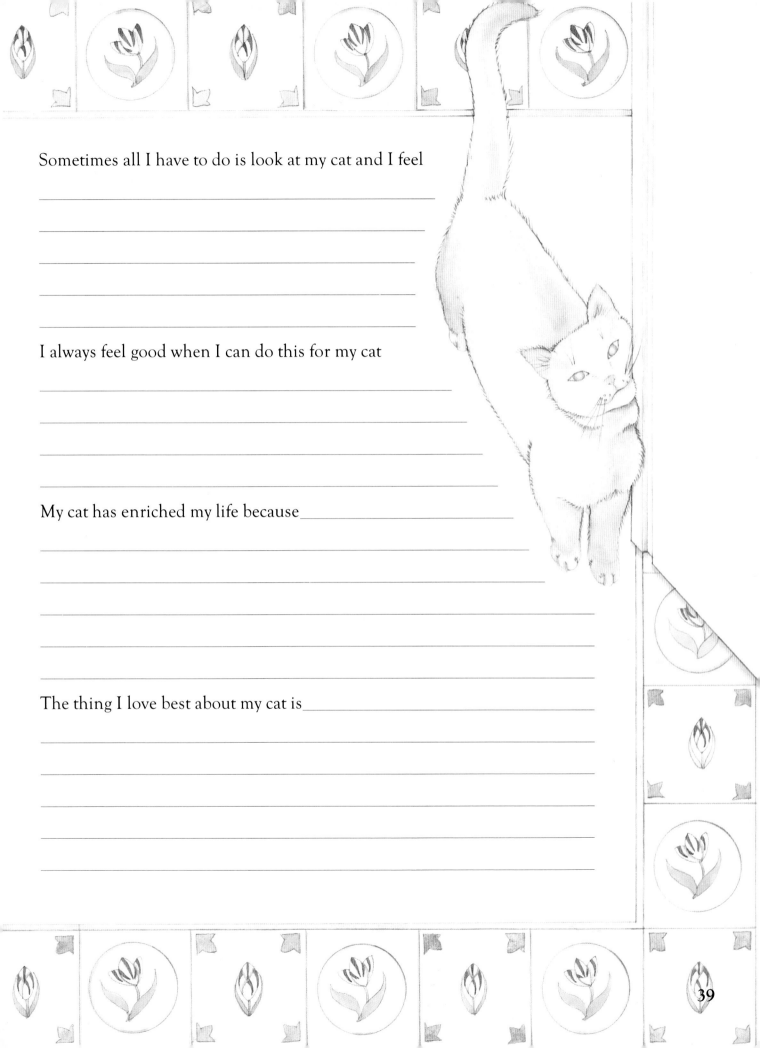

Our Special Moments Together

I need some peace and comfort
When I've had a long, hard day.
So I stretch out with my cat
And my cares just melt away.

I pamper my cat by

_____

_____

_____

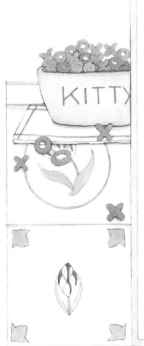

A SPECIAL PICTURE
OF ME AND MY CAT

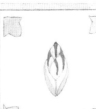

My cat purrs the most when I _____

_____

_____

_____

The spot my cat loves best to be scratched is

_____

_____

_____

My cat can't resist when I _____

_____

_____

_____

I fall in love with my cat all over again each time _____

_____

_____

_____

_____

My cat helps make the world a special place for me because _____

_____

_____

_____

_____

Name _____

Relationship _____

And a few words about my cat _____

_____

_____

_____

_____

_____

PICTURE WITH
MY CAT

PICTURE WITH
MY CAT

People Who Love My Cat

Yes, my friends all agree
My cat's dear in every way.
Here's a picture with kind words
They were good enough to say.

Name_____

Relationship_____

And a few words about my cat_____

_____

_____

_____

_____

_____

Name _____

Relationship _____

And a few words about my cat _____

_____

_____

_____

_____

_____

PICTURE WITH
MY CAT

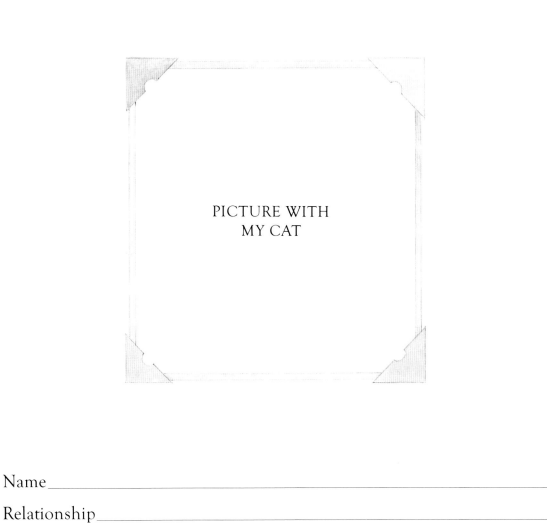

PICTURE WITH
MY CAT

Name_____

Relationship_____

And a few words about my cat_____

_____

_____

_____

_____

_____

Trips We've Taken

On the road to fun,
Just couldn't say goodbye.
So we took the trip together,
This wee traveler and I.

In the car, my cat _____

_____

_____

_____

On planes and trains, my cat _____

_____

_____

_____

_____

What I remember most about a trip with my cat is _____

_____

_____

_____

_____

When we get home, the first thing my cat does is _____

_____

_____

_____

_____

If I ever go on another trip with my cat, I plan to _____

_____

_____

_____

_____

If I can't take my cat with me, I _____

_____

_____

_____

_____

_____

PERMIT ONE
PERMIT 1 one CAT

47

I'll Always Remember

Happiness and love
All rolled into one.
Cuddly and warm
A barrel of fun.

I laughed so hard the time my cat _____

_____

_____

_____

I got so mad the time my cat _____

_____

_____

_____

I was scared the time my cat _____

_____

_____

_____

I was so relieved when my cat _____

_____

_____

_____

_____

I cried when my cat _____

_____

_____

_____

_____

I was so happy the time my cat _____

_____

_____

_____

_____

When My Cat Is Sick

*Doesn't choose to eat at all
And wants to be left alone.
I know my cat isn't feeling well,
So I get the vet on the phone.*

I can tell my cat's not feeling well when _____

_____

_____

_____

_____

To make my cat feel better I always _____

_____

_____

_____

Once I was really worried when my cat _____

_____

_____

_____

My cat's reaction to visiting the vet is _____

_____

_____

_____

My best method for giving my cat medicine is _____

_____

_____

_____

One emergency my cat and I experienced was _____

_____

_____

_____

_____

Veterinarian's name

_____

Address/Phone_____

_____

_____

Date of visit _____ Cat's age _____
Reason for visit _____

_____

Result _____

_____

_____

Our next appointment is_____

Date of visit _____ Cat's age _____
Reason for visit _____

_____

Result _____

_____

_____

Our next appointment is_____

My Cat's Health Records

*H*ere I'll keep a record
So I'll never forget:
The shots, and the boosters,
Our trips to the vet.

Date of visit_____ Cat's age_____

Reason for visit_____

_____

Result_____

_____

_____

Our next appointment is_____

Date of visit_____ Cat's age_____

Reason for visit_____

_____

Result_____

_____

_____

Our next appointment is_____

53

Veterinarian's name

_____

Address/Phone _____

_____

_____

Date of visit _____ Cat's age _____

Reason for visit _____

_____

Result _____

_____

_____

Our next appointment is _____

Date of visit _____ Cat's age _____

Reason for visit _____

_____

Result _____

_____

_____

Our next appointment is _____

Date of visit_____ Cat's age_____

Reason for visit_____

_____

Result _____

_____

_____

Our next appointment is_____

Date of visit_____ Cat's age_____

Reason for visit_____

_____

Result _____

_____

_____

Our next appointment is_____

Date of visit_____ Cat's age_____

Reason for visit_____

_____

Result _____

_____

_____

Our next appointment is_____

Veterinarian's name
_____

Address/Phone_____
_____
_____

Date of visit _____ Cat's age _____

Reason for visit _____
_____

Result _____
_____
_____

Our next appointment is_____

Date of visit _____ Cat's age _____

Reason for visit _____
_____

Result _____
_____
_____

Our next appointment is_____

Date of visit _____ Cat's age _____

Reason for visit _____

_____

Result _____

_____

_____

Our next appointment is _____

Date of visit _____ Cat's age _____

Reason for visit _____

_____

Result _____

_____

_____

Our next appointment is _____

Date of visit _____ Cat's age _____

Reason for visit _____

_____

Result _____

_____

_____

Our next appointment is _____

Picture Purrfect

My cat is beautiful,
Simply divine.
I cherish these pictures
Of this love of mine.

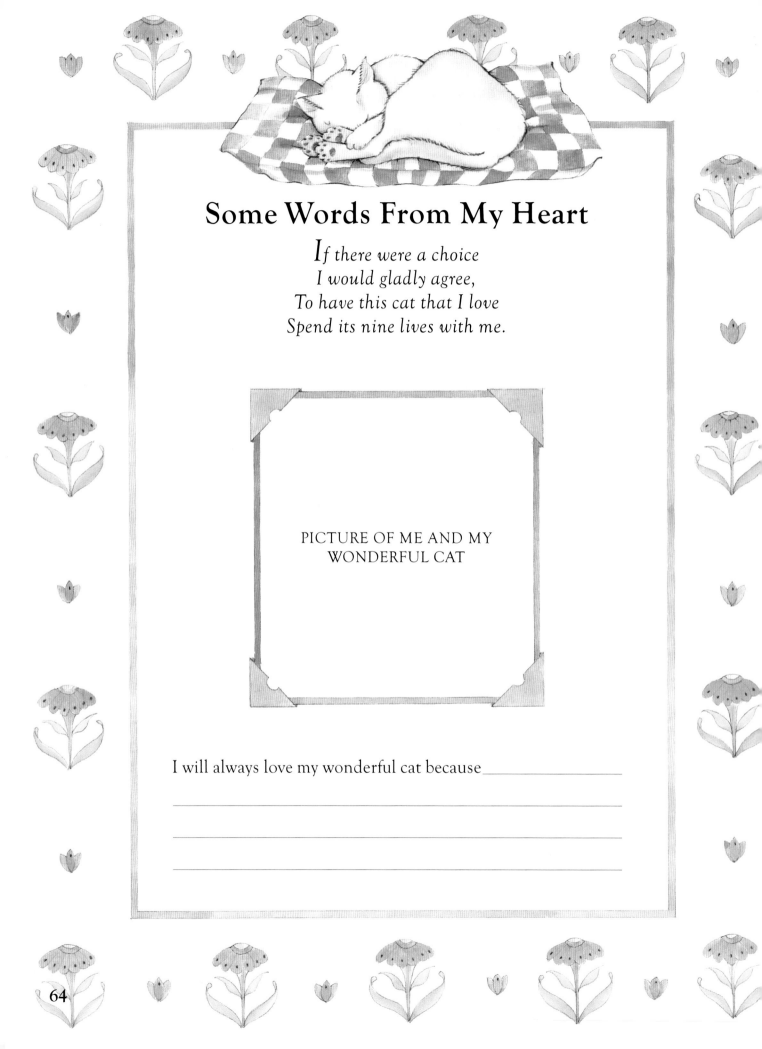

Some Words From My Heart

If there were a choice
I would gladly agree,
To have this cat that I love
Spend its nine lives with me.

PICTURE OF ME AND MY
WONDERFUL CAT

I will always love my wonderful cat because_____

_____

_____

_____